LEARNING THE TWO TIMES TABLE

One times two is two	1 x 2 = 2
Two twos are four	2 x 2 = 4
Three twos are six	3 x 2 = 6
Four twos are eight	4 x 2 = 8
Five twos are ten	5 x 2 = 10
Six twos are twelve	6 x 2 = 12
Seven twos are fourteen	7 x 2 = 14
Eight twos are sixteen	8 x 2 = 16
Nine twos are eighteen	9 x 2 = 18
Ten twos are twenty	10 x 2 = 20

Some people like to learn eleven times two and twelve times two:

Eleven twos are twenty-two	11 x 2 = 22
Twelve twos are twenty-four	12 x 2 = 24

What about zero times two?

Zero times two is zero.

Minnie

Max

Zero times two is zero	0 x 2 = 0

Read the two times table. Now try saying it without reading it.
Keep saying it over and over again.

Fill in the missing numbers:

3 x 2 = ☐	7 x 2 = ☐	9 x 2 = ☐	4 x 2 = ☐
6 x 2 = ☐	2 x 2 = ☐	8 x 2 = ☐	
0 x 2 = ☐	10 x 2 = ☐	1 x 2 = ☐	5 x 2 = ☐

Fill in the missing answers:

7 x 2 = ☐

5 x 2 = ☐

2 x 2 = ☐

8 x 2 = ☐

11 x 2 = ☐

3 x 2 = ☐

10 x 2 = ☐

9 x 2 = ☐

4 x 2 = ☐

0 x 2 = ☐

6 x 2 = ☐

12 x 2 = ☐

Draw lines to join the questions to the answers:

9 x 2   16

5 x 2   6

2 x 2   8

8 x 2   20

7 x 2   14

4 x 2   2

3 x 2   18

6 x 2   0

1 x 2   4

10 x 2   10

0 x 2   12

See how quickly you can write out the two times table up to ten times two.

The table has been started for you.

1 x 2 = 2
2 x 2 = 4

2

LEARNING THE THREE TIMES TABLE

One times three is three	1 x 3 = 3
Two threes are six	2 x 3 = 6
Three threes are nine	3 x 3 = 9
Four threes are twelve	4 x 3 = 12
Five threes are fifteen	5 x 3 = 15
Six threes are eighteen	6 x 3 = 18
Seven threes are twenty-one	7 x 3 = 21
Eight threes are twenty-four	8 x 3 = 24
Nine threes are twenty-seven	9 x 3 = 27
Ten threes are thirty	10 x 3 = 30

Some people like to learn eleven times three and twelve times three:

Eleven threes are thirty-three	11 x 3 = 33
Twelve threes are thirty-six	12 x 3 = 36

 What's zero times three? Zero times three is zero.

Zero times three is zero	0 x 3 = 0

Read the three times table. Can you say it without reading it?
Keep saying it over and over again.

Fill in the missing numbers:

10 x 3 = ☐   4 x 3 = ☐   7 x 3 = ☐   2 x 3 = ☐

6 x 3 = ☐   0 x 3 = ☐   8 x 3 = ☐

5 x 3 = ☐   1 x 3 = ☐   9 x 3 = ☐   3 x 3 = ☐

Fill in the missing answers:

6 x 3 = ☐

2 x 3 = ☐   4 x 3 = ☐

9 x 3 = ☐   10 x 3 = ☐

12 x 3 = ☐   8 x 3 = ☐

7 x 3 = ☐   11 x 3 = ☐

0 x 3 = ☐   5 x 3 = ☐

              3 x 3 = ☐

Draw lines to join the questions to the answers:

4 x 3	15
8 x 3	3
5 x 3	12
10 x 3	0
1 x 3	24
7 x 3	6
0 x 3	27
6 x 3	30
2 x 3	9
9 x 3	18
3 x 3	21

See how quickly you can write out the three times table up to ten times three.

The table has been started for you.

1 x 3 = 3

LEARNING THE FOUR TIMES TABLE

One times four is four	1 x 4 = 4
Two fours are eight	2 x 4 = 8
Three fours are twelve	3 x 4 = 12
Four fours are sixteen	4 x 4 = 16
Five fours are twenty	5 x 4 = 20
Six fours are twenty-four	6 x 4 = 24
Seven fours are twenty-eight	7 x 4 = 28
Eight fours are thirty-two	8 x 4 = 32
Nine fours are thirty-six	9 x 4 = 36
Ten fours are forty	10 x 4 = 40

Some people like to learn eleven times four and twelve times four:

Eleven fours are forty-four	11 x 4 = 44
Twelve fours are forty-eight	12 x 4 = 48

Zero times four is ....

Zero.

Zero times four is zero	0 x 4 = 0

Read the four times table.
Keep saying it over and over again.

Fill in the missing numbers:

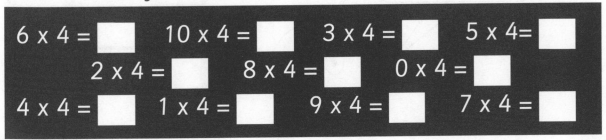

6 x 4 = ☐   10 x 4 = ☐   3 x 4 = ☐   5 x 4= ☐

2 x 4 = ☐   8 x 4 = ☐   0 x 4 = ☐

4 x 4 = ☐   1 x 4 = ☐   9 x 4 = ☐   7 x 4 = ☐

PRACTISING THE FOUR TIMES TABLE

Fill in the missing answers:

3 x 4 = ☐

9 x 4 = ☐

12 x 4 = ☐

2 x 4 = ☐

6 x 4 = ☐

11 x 4 = ☐

5 x 4 = ☐

0 x 4 = ☐

10 x 4 = ☐

8 x 4 = ☐

4 x 4 = ☐

7 x 4 = ☐

Draw lines to join the questions to the answers:

6 x 4	40
1 x 4	4
9 x 4	12
3 x 4	24
4 x 4	20
10 x 4	32
2 x 4	36
8 x 4	8
5 x 4	16
7 x 4	0
0 x 4	28

See how quickly you can write out the four times table up to ten times four.

The table has been started for you.

1 x 4 = 4

6

LEARNING THE FIVE TIMES TABLE

One times five is five	1 x 5 = 5
Two fives are ten	2 x 5 = 10
Three fives are fifteen	3 x 5 = 15
Four fives are twenty	4 x 5 = 20
Five fives are twenty-five	5 x 5 = 25
Six fives are thirty	6 x 5 = 30
Seven fives are thirty-five	7 x 5 = 35
Eight fives are forty	8 x 5 = 40
Nine fives are forty-five	9 x 5 = 45
Ten fives are fifty	10 x 5 = 50
Eleven fives are fifty-five	11 x 5 = 55
Twelve fives are sixty	12 x 5 = 60
Zero times five is zero	0 x 5 = 0

 What do you notice about the five times table?

The answer always ends with a five or a zero.

Did you know that the answer to any multiplication is always called the **product**?

Fill in the missing products:

5 10 15 ☐ 25 30 ☐ 40 45 ☐ 55 60

3 x 5 = ☐   7 x 5 = ☐   4 x 5 = ☐   9 x 5 = ☐

PRACTISING THE FIVE TIMES TABLE

Fill in the missing answers:

12 x 5 = ☐

5 x 5 = ☐   6 x 5 = ☐

0 x 5 = ☐   11 x 5 = ☐

8 x 5 = ☐   2 x 5 = ☐

3 x 5 = ☐   7 x 5 = ☐

10 x 5 = ☐   4 x 5 = ☐

              9 x 5 = ☐

Draw lines to join the questions to the answers:

9 x 5	25
5 x 5	0
2 x 5	10
8 x 5	30
0 x 5	50
6 x 5	45
3 x 5	20
10 x 5	5
4 x 5	15
7 x 5	40
1 x 5	35

See how quickly you can write out the five times table up to ten times five.

The table has been started for you.

1 x 5 = 5

LEARNING THE SIX TIMES TABLE

One times six is six	1 x 6 = 6
Two sixes are twelve	2 x 6 = 12
Three sixes are eighteen	3 x 6 = 18
Four sixes are twenty-four	4 x 6 = 24
Five sixes are thirty	5 x 6 = 30
Six sixes are thirty-six	6 x 6 = 36
Seven sixes are forty-two	7 x 6 = 42
Eight sixes are forty-eight	8 x 6 = 48
Nine sixes are fifty-four	9 x 6 = 54
Ten sixes are sixty	10 x 6 = 60

Some people like to learn eleven times six and twelve times six:

Eleven sixes are sixty-six	11 x 6 = 66
Twelve sixes are seventy-two	12 x 6 = 72

 What is the product of six and zero? Zero.

Zero times six is zero	0 x 6 = 0

Read the six times table.
Say it again and again.

Fill in the missing numbers:

6 x 6 = ☐   2 x 6 = ☐   10 x 6 = ☐   8 x 6 = ☐

3 x 6 = ☐   7 x 6 = ☐   4 x 6 = ☐

0 x 6 = ☐   5 x 6 = ☐   1 x 6 = ☐   9 x 6 = ☐

PRACTISING THE SIX TIMES TABLE

Fill in the missing answers:

10 x 6 = ☐

3 x 6 = ☐   2 x 6 = ☐

7 x 6 = ☐   1 x 6 = ☐

11 x 6 = ☐   9 x 6 = ☐

4 x 6 = ☐   5 x 6 = ☐

12 x 6 = ☐   8 x 6 = ☐

                  6 x 6 = ☐

Draw lines to join the questions to the answers:

2 x 6	24
5 x 6	18
9 x 6	12
4 x 6	42
8 x 6	0
0 x 6	6
6 x 6	30
3 x 6	48
1 x 6	60
7 x 6	36
10 x 6	54

See how quickly you can write out the six times table up to ten times six.

The table has been started for you.

1 x 6 = 6

LEARNING THE SEVEN TIMES TABLE

One times seven is seven	1 x 7 = 7
Two sevens are fourteen	2 x 7 = 14
Three sevens are twenty-one	3 x 7 = 21
Four sevens are twenty-eight	4 x 7 = 28
Five sevens are thirty-five	5 x 7 = 35
Six sevens are forty-two	6 x 7 = 42
Seven sevens are forty-nine	7 x 7 = 49
Eight sevens are fifty-six	8 x 7 = 56
Nine sevens are sixty-three	9 x 7 = 63
Ten sevens are seventy	10 x 7 = 70

Some people like to learn eleven times seven and twelve times seven:

Eleven sevens are seventy-seven	11 x 7 = 77
Twelve sevens are eighty-four	12 x 7 = 84

Zero times any number is zero.

So zero times seven is zero.

Zero times seven is zero	0 x 7 = 0

Keep practising the seven times table.

Fill in the missing numbers:

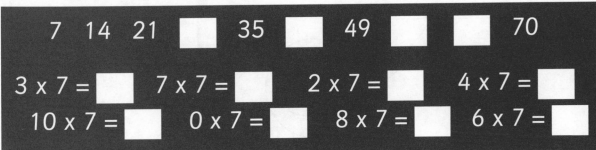

7   14   21   ☐   35   ☐   49   ☐   ☐   70

3 x 7 = ☐   7 x 7 = ☐   2 x 7 = ☐   4 x 7 = ☐

10 x 7 = ☐   0 x 7 = ☐   8 x 7 = ☐   6 x 7 = ☐

PRACTISING THE SEVEN TIMES TABLE

Fill in the missing answers:

9 x 7 = ☐

2 x 7 = ☐   10 x 7 = ☐

5 x 7 = ☐   3 x 7 = ☐

1 x 7 = ☐   12 x 7 = ☐

8 x 7 = ☐   7 x 7 = ☐

6 x 7 = ☐   11 x 7 = ☐

                4 x 7 = ☐

Draw lines to join the questions to the answers:

7 x 7	70
9 x 7	28
1 x 7	42
4 x 7	7
6 x 7	56
2 x 7	49
10 x 7	14
5 x 7	21
8 x 7	0
0 x 7	63
3 x 7	35

See how quickly you can write out the seven times table up to ten times seven.

Start with 1 x 7.

LEARNING THE EIGHT TIMES TABLE

One times eight is eight	1 x 8 = 8
Two eights are sixteen	2 x 8 = 16
Three eights are twenty-four	3 x 8 = 24
Four eights are thirty-two	4 x 8 = 32
Five eights are forty	5 x 8 = 40
Six eights are forty-eight	6 x 8 = 48
Seven eights are fifty-six	7 x 8 = 56
Eight eights are sixty-four	8 x 8 = 64
Nine eights are seventy-two	9 x 8 = 72
Ten eights are eighty	10 x 8 = 80

Some people like to learn eleven times eight and twelve times eight:

Eleven eights are eighty-eight	11 x 8 = 88
Twelve eights are ninety-six	12 x 8 = 96

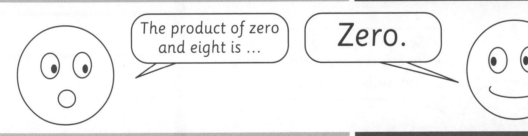

The product of zero and eight is …

Zero.

Zero times eight is zero	0 x 8 = 0

Keep reading the eight times table to learn it.

Fill in the missing numbers:

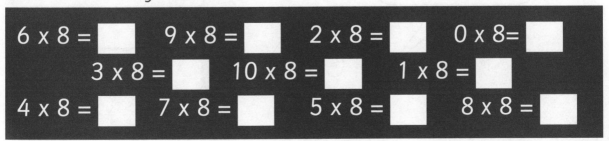

6 x 8 = ☐   9 x 8 = ☐   2 x 8 = ☐   0 x 8 = ☐

3 x 8 = ☐   10 x 8 = ☐   1 x 8 = ☐

4 x 8 = ☐   7 x 8 = ☐   5 x 8 = ☐   8 x 8 = ☐

PRACTISING THE EIGHT TIMES TABLE

Fill in the missing answers:

8 x 8 = ☐

5 x 8 = ☐   4 x 8 = ☐

2 x 8 = ☐   10 x 8 = ☐

12 x 8 = ☐   6 x 8 = ☐

7 x 8 = ☐   3 x 8 = ☐

11 x 8 = ☐   9 x 8 = ☐

1 x 8 = ☐

Draw lines to join the questions to the answers:

10 x 8	32
2 x 8	0
0 x 8	48
6 x 8	16
9 x 8	24
4 x 8	8
7 x 8	80
3 x 8	40
8 x 8	56
1 x 8	72
5 x 8	64

See how quickly you can write out the eight times table up to ten times eight.

Start with 1 x 8.

LEARNING THE NINE TIMES TABLE

One times nine is nine	$1 \times 9 = 9$
Two nines are eighteen	$2 \times 9 = 18$
Three nines are twenty-seven	$3 \times 9 = 27$
Four nines are thirty-six	$4 \times 9 = 36$
Five nines are forty-five	$5 \times 9 = 45$
Six nines are fifty-four	$6 \times 9 = 54$
Seven nines are sixty-three	$7 \times 9 = 63$
Eight nines are seventy-two	$8 \times 9 = 72$
Nine nines are eighty-one	$9 \times 9 = 81$
Ten nines are ninety	$10 \times 9 = 90$
Eleven nines are ninety-nine	$11 \times 9 = 99$
Twelve nines are one hundred and eight	$12 \times 9 = 108$
Zero times nine is zero	$0 \times 9 = 0$

 What are three nines?

 Nine add nine add nine. That's twenty-seven.

Fill in the missing numbers:

$7 \times 9 = \boxed{}$ $3 \times 9 = \boxed{}$ $1 \times 9 = \boxed{}$ $9 \times 9 = \boxed{}$

$4 \times 9 = \boxed{}$ $0 \times 9 = \boxed{}$ $2 \times 9 = \boxed{}$

$10 \times 9 = \boxed{}$ $8 \times 9 = \boxed{}$ $5 \times 9 = \boxed{}$ $6 \times 9 = \boxed{}$

PRACTISING THE NINE TIMES TABLE

Fill in the missing answers:

0 x 9 = ☐

7 x 9 = ☐   6 x 9 = ☐

5 x 9 = ☐   11 x 9 = ☐

2 x 9 = ☐   3 x 9 = ☐

12 x 9 = ☐   8 x 9 = ☐

10 x 9 = ☐   4 x 9 = ☐

9 x 9 = ☐

Draw lines to join the questions to the answers:

10 x 9	27
2 x 9	36
0 x 9	90
6 x 9	81
9 x 9	54
4 x 9	18
7 x 9	9
3 x 9	0
8 x 9	72
1 x 9	45
5 x 9	63

See how quickly you can write out the nine times table up to ten times nine.

You could time yourself with a watch or a clock.

16

LEARNING THE TEN TIMES TABLE

One times ten is ten	1 x 10 = 10
Two tens are twenty	2 x 10 = 20
Three tens are thirty	3 x 10 = 30
Four tens are forty	4 x 10 = 40
Five tens are fifty	5 x 10 = 50
Six tens are sixty	6 x 10 = 60
Seven tens are seventy	7 x 10 = 70
Eight tens are eighty	8 x 10 = 80
Nine tens are ninety	9 x 10 = 90
Ten tens are a hundred	10 x 10 = 100
Eleven tens are a hundred and ten	11 x 10 = 110
Twelve tens are a hundred and twenty	12 x 10 = 120
Zero times ten is zero	0 x 10 = 0

 The ten times table ...   ... is the easiest table to learn.

Fill in the missing numbers:

3 x 10 = ☐   6 x 10 = ☐   4 x 10 = ☐   0 x 10 = ☐

5 x 10 = ☐   8 x 10 = ☐   2 x 10 = ☐

9 x 10 = ☐   1 x 10 = ☐   7 x 10 = ☐   10 x 10 = ☐

PRACTISING THE TEN TIMES TABLE

Fill in the missing answers:

3 x 10 = ☐

5 x 10 = ☐   6 x 10 = ☐

2 x 10 = ☐   4 x 10 = ☐

12 x 10 = ☐   9 x 10 = ☐

7 x 10 = ☐   0 x 10 = ☐

11 x 10 = ☐   8 x 10 = ☐

10 x 10 = ☐

Draw lines to join the questions to the answers:

10 x 10	50
3 x 10	60
8 x 10	0
5 x 10	40
4 x 10	30
0 x 10	70
9 x 10	100
6 x 10	80
1 x 10	10
7 x 10	90
2 x 10	20

See how quickly you can write out the ten times table up to ten times ten.

Can you write it in less than one minute?

Some people like to learn the eleven times table and the twelve times table.

1 x 11	=	11
2 x 11	=	22
3 x 11	=	33
4 x 11	=	44
5 x 11	=	55
6 x 11	=	66
7 x 11	=	77
8 x 11	=	88
9 x 11	=	99
10 x 11	=	110
11 x 11	=	121
12 x 11	=	132

One times eleven is eleven

Two elevens are twenty-two

Three elevens are thirty-three

Four elevens are forty-four

Five elevens are fifty-five

Six elevens are sixty-six

Seven elevens are seventy-seven

Eight elevens are eighty-eight

Nine elevens are ninety-nine

Ten elevens are a hundred and ten

Eleven elevens are a hundred and twenty-one

Twelve elevens are a hundred and thirty-two

Fill in the missing numbers:

3 x 11 = ☐   7 x 11 = ☐   9 x 11 = ☐   0 x 11 = ☐

11 x 11 = ☐   8 x 11 = ☐   12 x 11 = ☐

4 x 11 = ☐   6 x 11 = ☐   10 x 11 = ☐

Fill in the missing products of eleven:

11 [ ] 33 [ ] [ ] [ ] 77 [ ] 99 [ ] 121 [ ]

Fill in the missing answers:

2 x 11 = [ ]

6 x 11 = [ ]

4 x 11 = [ ]

9 x 11 = [ ]

7 x 11 = [ ]

10 x 11 = [ ]

8 x 11 = [ ]

5 x 11 = [ ]

0 x 11 = [ ]

11 x 11 = [ ]

3 x 11 = [ ]

12 x 11 = [ ]

1 x 11 = [ ]

Write out the eleven times table as quickly as you can.

LEARNING THE TWELVE TIMES TABLE

Don't forget, zero times twelve must be zero.

1 x 12	=	12
2 x 12	=	24
3 x 12	=	36
4 x 12	=	48
5 x 12	=	60
6 x 12	=	72
7 x 12	=	84
8 x 12	=	96
9 x 12	=	108
10 x 12	=	120
11 x 12	=	132
12 x 12	=	144

One times twelve is twelve
Two twelves are twenty-four
Three twelves are thirty-six
Four twelves are forty-eight
Five twelves are sixty
Six twelves are seventy-two
Seven twelves are eighty-four
Eight twelves are ninety-six
Nine twelves are a hundred and eight
Ten twelves are a hundred and twenty
Eleven twelves are a hundred and thirty-two
Twelve twelves are a hundred and forty-four

Fill in the missing numbers:

☐ x 12 = 84   ☐ x 12 = 36   ☐ x 12 = 132
☐ x 12 = 96   ☐ x 12 = 48   ☐ x 12 = 144
☐ x 12 = 0   ☐ x 12 = 60   ☐ x 12 = 120

PRACTISING THE TWELVE TIMES TABLE

Fill in the missing products of twelve:

12 [ ] 36 [ ] 60 [ ] 84 96 [ ] [ ] [ ] 144

Fill in the missing answers:

6 x 12 = [ ]

1 x 12 = [ ]

9 x 12 = [ ]

4 x 12 = [ ]

12 x 12 = [ ]

7 x 12 = [ ]

2 x 12 = [ ]

10 x 12 = [ ]

0 x 12 = [ ]

8 x 12 = [ ]

5 x 12 = [ ]

11 x 12 = [ ]

3 x 12 = [ ]

Write out the twelve times table as quickly as you can.

22

Time yourself on each table up to 10 x

2 x table

	X		=	
	X		=	
	X		=	
	X		=	
	X		=	
	X		=	
	X		=	
	X		=	
	X		=	
	X		=	

Time taken:

☐ seconds

3 x table

	X		=	
	X		=	
	X		=	
	X		=	
	X		=	
	X		=	
	X		=	
	X		=	
	X		=	
	X		=	

Time taken:

☐ seconds

4 x table

	X		=	
	X		=	
	X		=	
	X		=	
	X		=	
	X		=	
	X		=	
	X		=	
	X		=	
	X		=	

Time taken:

☐ seconds

5 x table

	X		=	
	X		=	
	X		=	
	X		=	
	X		=	
	X		=	
	X		=	
	X		=	
	X		=	
	X		=	

Time taken:

☐ seconds

6 x table

	X		=	
	X		=	
	X		=	
	X		=	
	X		=	
	X		=	
	X		=	
	X		=	
	X		=	
	X		=	

Time taken:

☐ seconds

7 x table

	X		=	
	X		=	
	X		=	
	X		=	
	X		=	
	X		=	
	X		=	
	X		=	
	X		=	
	X		=	

Time taken:

☐ seconds

8 x table

X   =
X   =
X   =
X   =
X   =
X   =
X   =
X   =
X   =
X   =

Time taken: [ ] seconds

9 x table

X   =
X   =
X   =
X   =
X   =
X   =
X   =
X   =
X   =
X   =

Time taken: [ ] seconds

10 x table

X   =
X   =
X   =
X   =
X   =
X   =
X   =
X   =
X   =
X   =

Time taken: [ ] seconds

11 x table

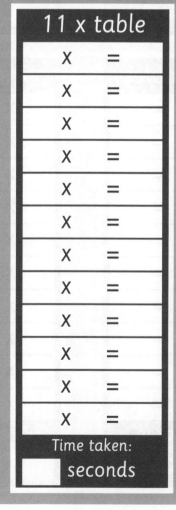

X   =
X   =
X   =
X   =
X   =
X   =
X   =
X   =
X   =
X   =
X   =
X   =

Time taken: [ ] seconds

12 x table

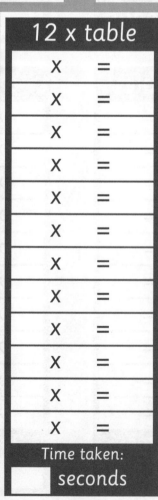

X   =
X   =
X   =
X   =
X   =
X   =
X   =
X   =
X   =
X   =
X   =
X   =

Time taken: [ ] seconds